A RECIPE FOR GOOD FUN

THE FINAL FRONTIER

Space explorers travel to dark, quiet and gloomy places without gravity... why would you ever go there on a Sunday afternoon? But even in space, adventure and great fun await! Can you match each circled astronaut with their location in the space scene below?

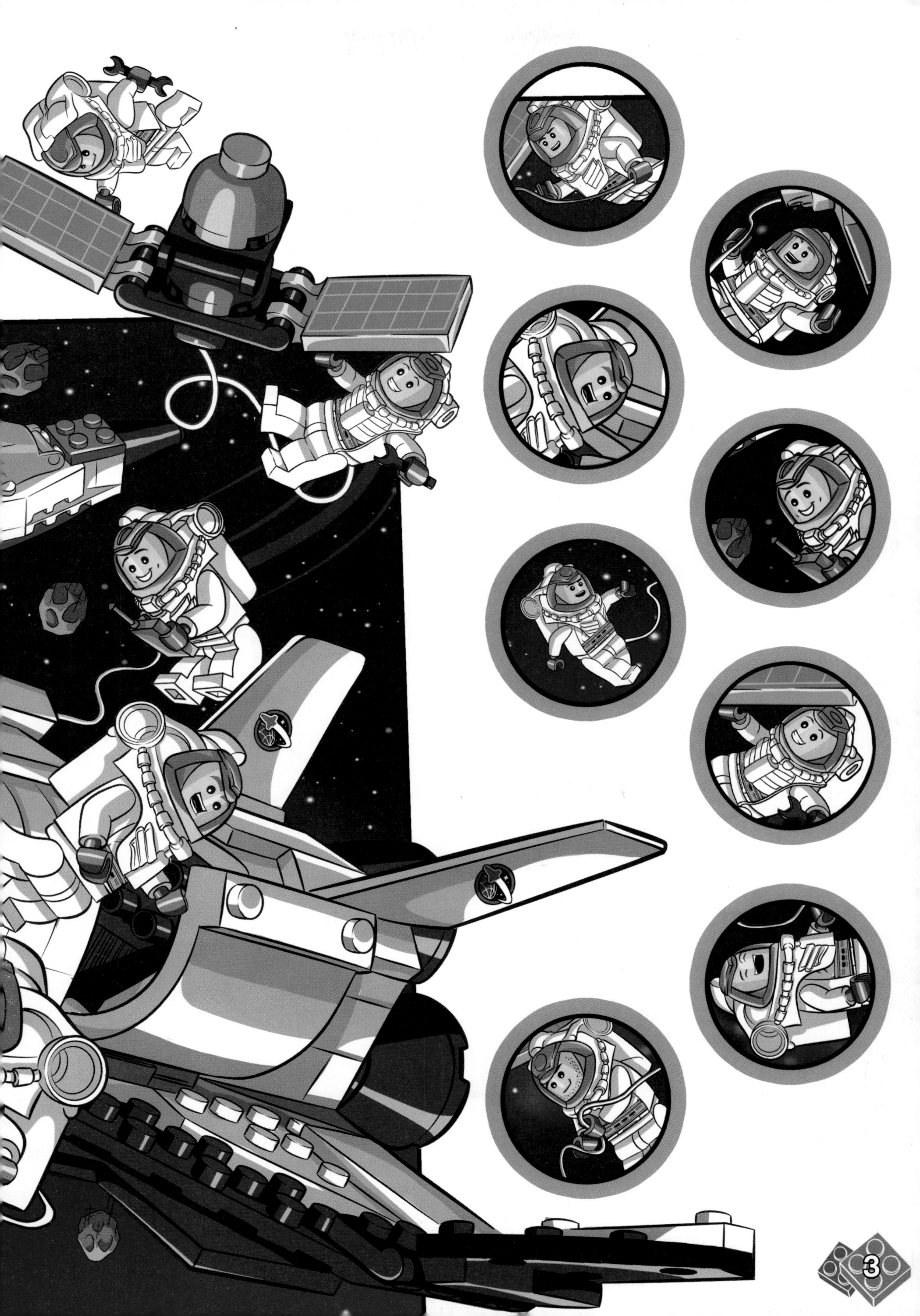

SAVE THAT SATELLITE!

As the sun rose over LEGO City Space Centre, one scientist discovered a problem that no one could have imagined.

"Sir," the scientist called out to his boss. "It seems that all of our screens are... blank?"

"Are you saying what I think you're saying?" asked the head scientist.

"Gulp! Yes, sir," he answered nervously. "Satellite G-04-L is offline."

The entire control room gasped.

Outside on the launch pad, workers scrambled to get the utility shuttle in place. Trucks filled the rockets with fuel and supplies.

"Hey, do you know what they say about this space shuttle?" one worker asked another.

"What?"

"It's out of this world!" the worker said with laugh.

"There's no time for jokes," the head scientist announced over the loudspeaker. "We have T minus 2 hours to get Satellite G-04-L back online, or else... we're in serious trouble..."

The workers set back to their tasks, but the astronauts were nowhere to be found.

“We’re almost ready,” said the head scientist as he searched the Space Centre. “Where are those astronauts!”

He finally found them eating pizza in the cafeteria. “No! No! No! I said it was launch time, not lunch time!”

The astronauts quickly changed into their spacesuits and boarded the shuttle. As soon as they were locked in safely, the countdown began.

The rockets roared to life and the shuttle raced up, up and away into the blue sky. From the cockpit, the crew could see the white clouds disappear as they exited the atmosphere. In minutes, the shuttle left the Earth behind and entered outer space.

"Space Centre, we are approaching Satellite G-04-L now," announced the captain. "We will attempt a space walk first to hook the target."

"Roger that," assured the captain. "This should be a cake walk."

"We're walking on cake?" asked the astronaut preparing for the mission. "I thought it was a space walk?"

"Get your helmet on and attach this rope to that satellite," commanded the captain. "Then it won't float away."

The astronaut put on her gold helmet and entered the cargo bay. The door closed behind her as the cargo bay doors opened and she floated up into the zero gravity of outer space.

The stars sparkled brightly in the darkness, as Earth sat quietly beneath her. It looked beautiful. But there was a job to do. The astronaut manoeuvred herself towards the satellite and successfully attached the rope. "Okay. Initiate phase two!"

Suddenly a giant yellow crane reached out of the cargo bay and clasped the satellite carefully. It then moved the satellite over the shuttle as the astronauts floated out with different tools. They opened the satellite and discovered the problem.

"Space Centre, G-04-L has blown its yellow card," said the captain.

"Can you fix it, Captain?" asked the head scientist.

"Of course we can," said the captain. "We have a substitute here." He slid the damaged card out and swiftly replaced it. The satellite came back to life with lights beeping and the antennas whirring again. "It should be fully operational, Space Centre. Let us know if the important communication comes through."

Back on Earth, the scientists switched on their main screen that stretched across the control room. At first white static erupted, but then something came into focus. It was a football match!

"The most important game in the history of LEGO City is online again!" cheered everyone in the control room.

"Mission accomplished!" radioed the head scientist.

"You've got Satellite ... GOOOOOOAAAALLLLL!!!!"

"What did you say, Space Centre?" asked the captain.

"Sorry," said the head scientist. "My team just scored."

At last, Satellite G-04-L was back in action, thanks to the hard-working team at LEGO City Space Centre.

"Hey guys!" said the captain. "If we head back now, we might be home in time for the second half!"

TROUBLE IN ORBIT

This astronaut has to fix a broken weather satellite. He only has a little oxygen left, so must choose the quickest path. Add up the numbers – the smallest total sum will show you the fastest way to go.

A SUIT FOR SPACE

The colour and shape of the symbol on a spacesuit depends on its use. This special mission requires a specific outfit shown below. Find and mark the right parts of the suit to complete it.

SPACE ROCKS

The space expedition brought back four types of rocks. Can you prepare them for special research? Sort them on the shelf so that they don't repeat in any row or column by writing the correct numbers in the cabinet's empty spaces.

A SPECIAL WISH

BEFORE THE LAUNCH

Before the space shuttle launches into Earth's orbit, check out the whole space flight base! Take a close look at the picture and mark all the things that are wrong.

3 2 1

MISSION: EXPEDITION!

A space shuttle was sent to a recently discovered planet. The drop zones for researchers and their study equipment are: **D4**, **B1** and **E4**. Mark these zones on the map with a red X.

RIDE ON RADARS

"Test pilot to base! Test pilot to base! Base, come in! I have been picked up on the radar. Which one shows my ship?"
Help the pilot and find his location on the right radar below.

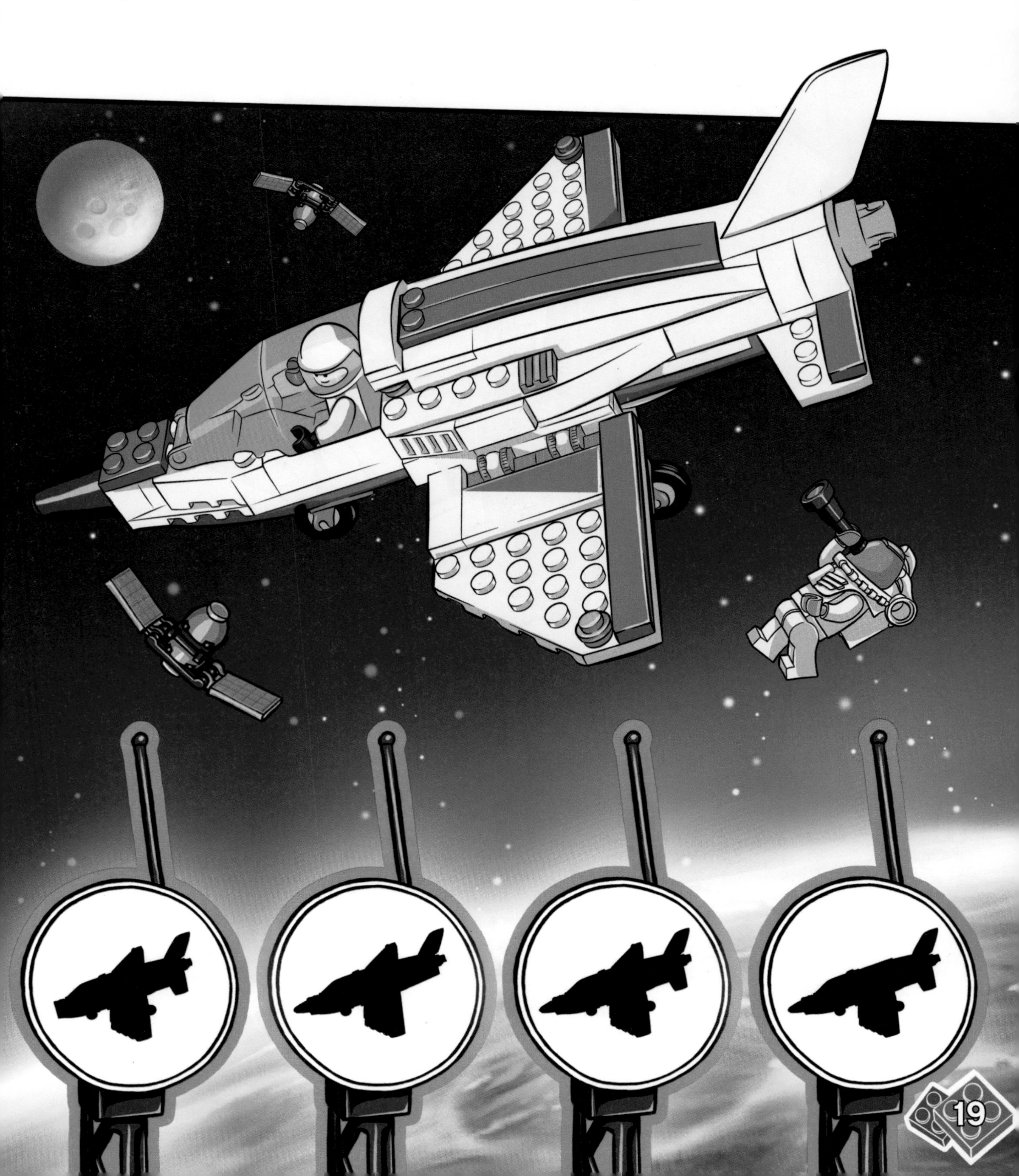

COSMIC RECREATION

Living in zero gravity is really cool!
Look at the picture pieces below, then mark which one doesn't belong in this space shuttle illustration.

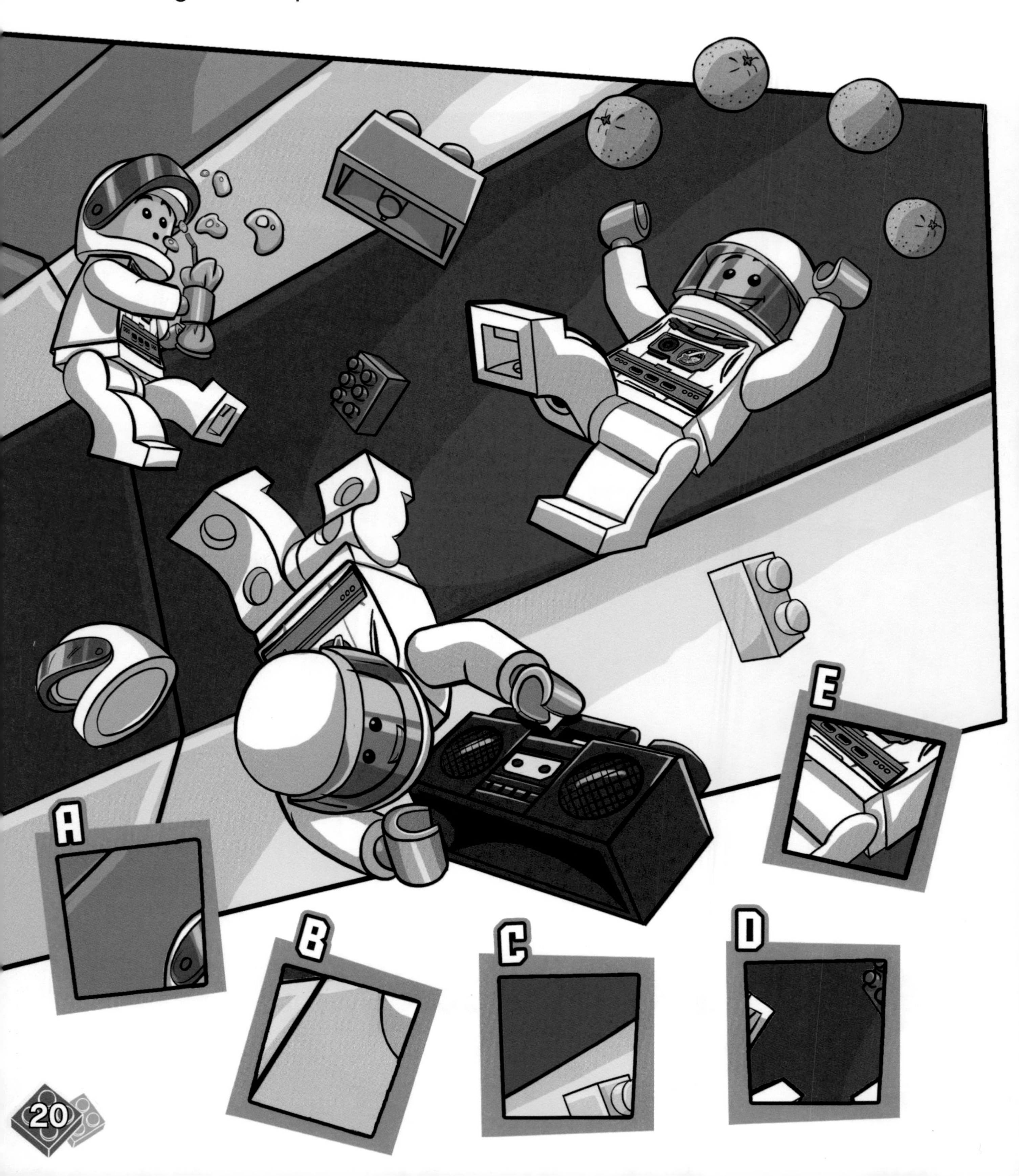

SHOWER CHALLENGE

Is it time for a bath? That's no small feat in space!
Order the pictures from 1 to 4 and see how the story ends.

THE CONQUEROR OF COSMOS

Sticking a flag into the surface of every new planet is already a tradition. What could a LEGO City astronaut flag look like? Design it! You should name the new planet, too!

A STRANGE PLANET

A swampy planet is not the best place to land a shuttle.
You need to scout the area!
Answer all the questions below with a YES or NO.

1. The planet is completely flat with no mountains.
2. One of the astronauts is trapped in the plants.
3. A newly discovered snake species has three horns.
4. There are seven astronauts in the picture.

ANSWERS

p. 2–3

p. 12

p. 13

p. 14

p. 16–17

p. 18

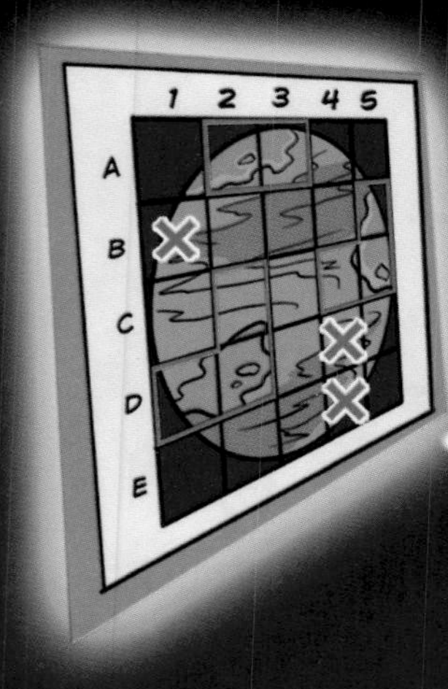

p. 19

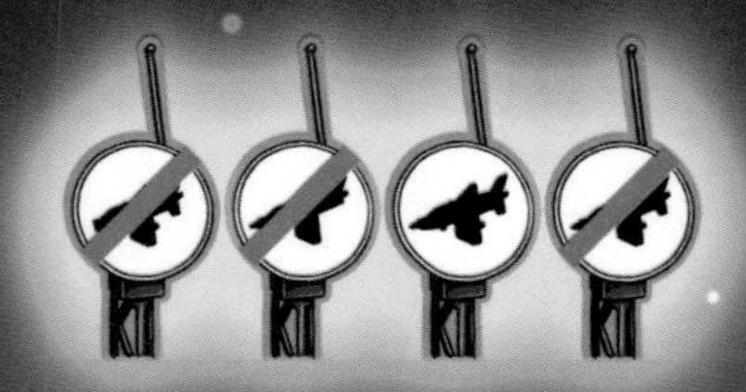

p. 20

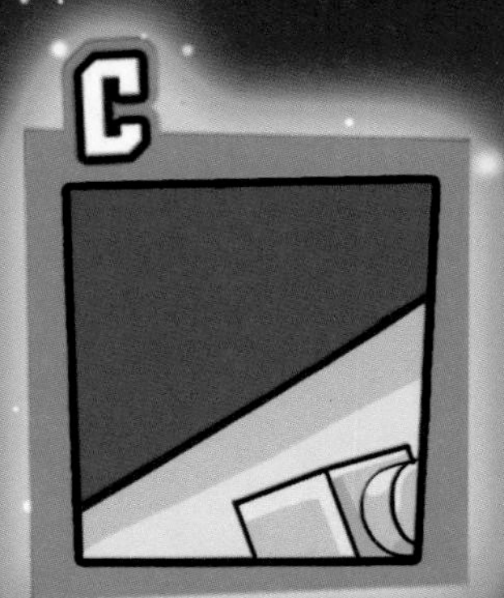

p. 21

p. 22

1. No 2. Yes 3. No 4. No